Romeo and Juliet

SHAKESPEARE

In the Original & Modern English

Perfection Learning®

Editorial Director	Julie Schumacher
Senior Editor	Rebecca Christian
Series Editor	Rebecca Burke
Editorial Assistant	Kate Winzenburg
Design Director	Randy Messer
Design	Mark Hagenberg, Deborah Bell
Cover Design	Tobi Cunningham
Production	Emily Greazel, Jane Wonderlin
Inside Illustration	Tom Rosborough

REVIEWERS

Helen Ann Fisher
Wheaton Christian High School
West Chicago, Illinois

Dorothy Franklin
Southwood High School
Shreveport, Louisiana

Jean Lorenzetti
Baker Junior High School
Fairborn, Ohio

Debbie Oxendine
South Robeson High School
Rowland, North Carolina

Dorcas Schudlich
Lutheran High School West
Detroit, Michigan

Kathy Stole
Urbandale High School
Urbandale, Iowa

FIELD-TESTERS

James M. Hurd
Peter Humphries Clark Academy
Cincinnati, Ohio

Robert Klimowski
Nathan Weeks Transitional School
Des Moines, Iowa

James P. Quinn
Staples High School
Westport, Connecticut

Barbara G. Reisner
American Fork High School
American Fork, Utah

©2004 Perfection Learning Corporation®
1000 North Second Avenue, P.O. Box 500
Logan, Iowa 51546-0500
Tel: 1-800-831-4190   Fax: 1-800-543-2745

ISBN-13: 978-0-7891-6212-0 ISBN-10: 0-7891-6212-1

23 24 25 26 27 PP 22 21 20 19 18

About the Author

Lou Barrett taught English at Staples High School in Westport, Connecticut. Honored as Westport Teacher of the Year, Lou had great success in reaching a wide spectrum of young people, from honor students to at-risk learners.

After doing undergraduate work at Brooklyn College, Hebrew Union College, and the University of Bridgeport, Lou was awarded her B.S. in education from Goddard College. She also earned a M.S. from Bank Street College of Education and a M.S. in special education from Columbia Teachers College.

Lou's teaching background is rich and varied. During her forty-two years in education, she worked with preschool children to high school students. She taught social studies and English, grades five through twelve. In addition, Lou also served as Director of Religious Education, Curriculum Director, and teacher at Temple Israel in Westport.

Besides authoring the Perfection Learning Parallel Text Workbooks, Lou is a published poet who received the Connecticut Poetry Society's Winchell Award.

Table of Contents *continued*

Act IV

Scene i
Setting the Stage	50
Reading Questions	50
Response Log	52

Scenes ii-iii
Setting the Stage	53
Reading Questions	54
Response Log	55

Scenes iv-v
Setting the Stage	56
Reading Questions	56
Response Log	58

Discussion Questions	60

Act V

Scene i
Setting the Stage	62
Reading Questions	62
Response Log	63

Scenes ii-iii
Setting the Stage	64
Reading Questions	64
Response Log	67

Discussion Questions	68

Action Chart	70
Extension Activities	73
Writing Activities	76

Introduction

You are about to read a famous play called *Romeo and Juliet*. This play was written by William Shakespeare about 400 years ago. Though it is an old play, you will find that you have much in common with the characters.

Your Parallel Text book and this workbook will help you understand the play. Here are four goals the book and workbook will help you reach.

1. You will learn about the characters and plot of a timeless work.
2. You will see how people and events compare to your own life and world.
3. You will understand the parts of a play and how they fit together.
4. You will compare the author's ideas and feelings about fate and love to your own.

How to Read the Parallel Text Book

Shakespeare wrote his plays in the late 1500s and early 1600s. The English language has changed significantly since then. As a result, readers today often find it hard to read Shakespeare's words.

The Parallel Text makes reading Shakespeare easier. That's because this text is rewritten into more modern speech.

The original version of the play appears in the Parallel Text on the pages on the left. These are the *even-numbered* pages (2, 4, 6, etc.). These pages show Shakespeare's actual words.

The modern version is printed on the right-hand pages. These are the *odd-numbered* pages (1, 3, 5, etc.). These pages show the play in today's language.

The modern version matches Shakespeare's words line for line. You can compare the two versions by looking directly across the page.

Most activities in this workbook refer to the modern version.

continued

Introduction *continued*

Special Features of a Play

The Parallel Text has been written in modern language. However, it is still a challenge to understand the play. Look for the following special features within the play. These features can help make your reading easier and more enjoyable.

1. Footnotes: Important words and ideas are explained at the bottom of the even-numbered pages. Even though you are reading the odd-numbered pages, check out these footnotes. They will help you understand what is going on.

2. Dialogue: The speaking parts in a play are called the dialogue. Each character's part is clearly labeled so you can tell who is speaking.

3. Prologue: A prologue is an introduction. It gives the reader important background information. It also can set the tone and mood of the drama. A play can have several prologues. Usually they are at the beginning of an act. In *Romeo and Juliet*, there are prologues (spoken by the chorus) at the beginning of Acts I and II.

4. Chorus: The role of the chorus is to comment on the action of the play. The chorus is considered a character in the drama. Its role is somewhat like that of an announcer or narrator. The chorus will add to your understanding of the events and characters.

5. Acts and Scenes: A play is divided into acts, and acts are usually divided into scenes. There are five acts in *Romeo and Juliet*. The acts have between three and six scenes. Each scene has an introduction. The introduction is in *italicized* type. It tells which characters are on stage when the scene begins. The introduction can give the place and time of the action, too. It sometimes tells about such things as props the characters are carrying, weather conditions, or background sounds.

6. Stage Directions: The stage directions are instructions for the actors. These instructions are written in *italicized* type throughout the play. The stage directions tell who is entering or exiting during a scene. They also describe the actors' gestures, movements, or tone of voice.

Pattern of the Play

Acts and scenes from the *Romeo and Juliet Parallel Text* are listed below. Page numbers are for the modern version (*odd-numbered pages*). This list will help you see the play's structure.

Acts and Scenes	Parallel Text Pages	
Prologue	page	21
Act I	pages	23–85
Scene i	pages	23–43
Scene ii	pages	45–51
Scene iii	pages	53–61
Scene iv	pages	63–71
Scene v	pages	73–85
Act II	pages	93–151
Prologue	page	93
Scene i	pages	95–97
Scene ii	pages	99–113
Scene iii	pages	115–121
Scene iv	pages	123–141
Scene v	pages	143–147
Scene vi	pages	149–151
Act III	pages	159–221
Scene i	pages	159–173
Scene ii	pages	175–183
Scene iii	pages	185–197
Scene iv	pages	199–201
Scene v	pages	203–221
Act IV	pages	229–263
Scene i	pages	229–237
Scene ii	pages	239–243
Scene iii	pages	245–247
Scene iv	pages	249–251
Scene v	pages	253–263
Act V	pages	271–303
Scene i	pages	271–275
Scene ii	pages	277–279
Scene iii	pages	281–303

Character Chart

Most of the characters in the play are involved in a bitter conflict between two families. As you meet each character listed in the box below, decide if he or she supports the Capulets, the Montagues, or neither.

Place each character's name in the column that shows which side that person supports. A person who supports neither side should be put in the neutral column. Base your answers on the characters' feelings in Act I and Act II.

Next, write a word or phrase which identifies that character's role. An example has been done for you.

Romeo	Paris	Sampson
Juliet	Lady Capulet	Friar Lawrence
Lord Montague	Prince Escalus	Benvoilo
Tybalt	Lord Capulet	
Nurse	Mercutio	

Montagues' side		Capulets' side	
Name	Role	Name	Role
		Gregory	servant of Capulets

Neutral	
Name	Role

Prologue

Setting the Stage

Today, theater-goers are usually given a printed program. This program tells the audience about the playwright, the actors, and the play itself. Often the program gives a brief overview of the entire story.

However, in Elizabethan days, most people could not read. Moreover, printing was a new craft and few books existed. Therefore, playwrights offered their audience a prologue in place of a printed program. Elizabethan audiences listened carefully to the information in such prologues.

Reading Questions	Pages/lines

Directions: There are Reading Questions for each prologue and scene in the play. Read the questions *before* you read each scene. These questions will guide you to important facts and ideas as you read.

After you read the scene, return to the Reading Questions and write your responses.

> Before Act I there is a short prologue narrated by the chorus. This prologue tells where the play is set. It also reveals the problems the main characters will face and how the play will end.

1. The two families are fighting because _____   page 21, line 3

2. Who is involved in the fight besides the two families? _____   page 21, line 4

3. This is a sad story of a young couple's _____   page 21, line 9

4. The parents' anger is finally ended by _____   page 21, line 11

5. How many hours will it take for this story to be acted on the stage? _____   page 21, line 12

Act I, Scene i

Setting the Stage

In Italian city-states, noble families often feuded. Fights might be caused by an insult. Or families might disagree over land ownership. Other feuds might be caused by struggles for political power. Sometimes families feuded over religious loyalties. For example, some people were loyal to the Pope, and others were not. Whatever the cause, the feuds proved dangerous and destructive.

As you read the first scene, notice how the characters are affected by a family feud.

Reading Questions	**Pages/lines**

> *Romeo and Juliet* takes place in northern Italy in the early 1300s. The play opens on a Sunday on the streets of the city. Two Capulet servants, Sampson and Gregory, come onstage. They boast of their bravery and what they will do to their enemies. Soon their bragging will lead to fighting.

1. Scene i opens in the streets of _____ , which is a city in _____

   page 21, line 2

2. Two families in the play hate one another. These families are the _____ and the _____

   page 31, line 83

3. Prince Escalus breaks up a fight caused by the feud between the two families. He says that if a fight happens again, those in-volved will _____

   page 31, lines 84–90

4. Benvolio, Lord Montague, and Lady Montague discuss Romeo's mood. List three things they say about Romeo that show he is depressed. Write the page and line numbers for each answer in the column at the right.

   a. _____

   _____

   pages 33–35

---

b. _____

_____

c. _____

_____

5. Romeo confesses that he is sad and depressed because _____

_____

page 37,
lines 159–163

Act I, Scene i

Response Log

Directions: The Response Log appears after most sets of Reading Questions. This activity helps you think about what you have read. Follow the instructions given in each Response Log section.

Questions:

1. Write about the feud between the two families. What might have caused the conflict? How long do you think it has been going on? What might end the feud?

2. Think of a modern conflict or feud like the one in the play. It could be one from a book, TV show, movie, or current events. Or you could choose a conflict that involves people you know. Describe this conflict and explain how it has affected the people involved.

Act I, Scene ii

Setting the Stage

During the Middle Ages, girls from noble families were generally expected to marry young. A family was embarrassed if a daughter wasn't married by the time she was fifteen. Unmarried girls might be sent away to a convent to receive further training to be proper wives.

Marriages were usually arranged by the families of young people. Most of the time, the engaged couple didn't complain about the arrangements. Sometimes betrothals, or engagements, were made when the children were as young as three. However, they weren't expected to marry until they were teenagers.

In this scene, notice how a marriage proposal is made.

Reading Questions	**Pages/lines**

> Lord Capulet and young Paris, Capulet's distant relative, talk on a street in Verona. Paris makes an important request of Capulet.

1. Paris asks Capulet for permission to _____

    _____

    page 45, lines 6–7

2. What are two reasons that Capulet hesitates to give his permission to Paris?

    page 45, lines 7–15

    a. _____

    _____

    b. _____

    _____

continued

Act I, Scene ii

Reading Questions *Continued*

3. Benvolio tells Romeo, "Find a new infection in your eye, and the poison of the old infection will die." The "infection" Benvolio refers to is love.

   page 47, lines 49–50

   a. In this quotation, Benvolio is urging Romeo to _____

   _____

   b. How do you think Benvolio feels about love? _____

   _____

   _____

Response Log

Juliet is only thirteen years old. Yet her father is already planning her marriage.

How do you feel about people marrying that young today? What might be the good points and the bad points of marrying in your early teens?

In the columns below, list the advantages and disadvantages of an early marriage. Then share your lists with a partner. Be ready to discuss your thoughts with the class.

Advantages (+)	Disadvantages (-)

Act I, Scenes iii–iv

Setting the Stage

In Shakespeare's time, mothers from noble families commonly turned over the care of their infants to other women. These women, called *wet nurses,* were usually young peasant mothers. Often the children felt closer to their nurses than their own mothers.

In Scene iii, notice how Juliet's nurse speaks as though Juliet were her own child.

Reading Questions | **Pages/lines**

> In Scene iii, the audience meets Juliet. We are also introduced to Juliet's 28-year-old mother and her talkative nurse. The three women talk of marriage and children.

1. On pages 55 and 57 the Nurse talks about Juliet's childhood. Write two phrases below that show the Nurse is fond of Juliet. List the page and line numbers for each phrase in the column at the right.

   a. _____

   _____

   b. _____

   _____

2. The Nurse is impressed with Paris because _____   page 57, line 80

   _____

3. Lady Capulet says that Paris will make a fine husband because   page 59, lines 97–98

   _____

4. What does Juliet promise her mother? _____   page 59, lines 101–104

   _____

   _____

continued

Reading Questions *Continued*   **Pages/lines**

Now Romeo, Mercutio, and Benvolio are on their way to the banquet. Romeo's friends tease him about his feelings for Rosaline.

5. Romeo is afraid to go to the banquet because _____

_____

_____

page 67, lines 50–52
page 71,
lines 112–117

Act I, Scenes iii–iv

Response Log

Think about the most important qualities that you would look for in a person you might want to marry. On the diagram below, write phrases that describe your ideal mate. First respond alone. Then share your thoughts with your classmates.

From your list and the class list, choose the ten qualities *you* personally think are most important. Write them in the space provided and rank them in order of importance to you.

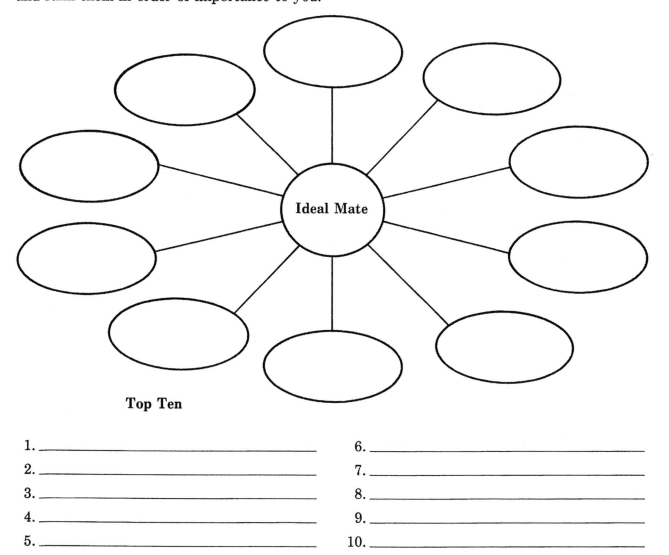

Top Ten

1. _____
2. _____
3. _____
4. _____
5. _____

6. _____
7. _____
8. _____
9. _____
10. _____

Act I, Scene v

Setting the Stage

The ways that a person "wins the heart" of another person in *Romeo and Juliet* are different from today. In the world of Romeo and Juliet, young women from noble families were kept away from boys. When a teenaged couple spent time together, they were carefully chaperoned. The meeting usually occurred in the young woman's home.

The language of young noble lovers was very formal, too. Love and marriage were considered holy. Therefore, lovers used words similar to those in a religious ceremony.

Notice how Romeo and Juliet speak to each other in religious terms when they first meet.

Reading Questions | **Pages/lines**

> Wearing masks, Romeo and his friends sneak into the Capulet banquet. Romeo has come to the party to find Rosaline. Juliet is there to get better acquainted with Paris. However, when Romeo and Juliet see each other, it is love at first sight.

1. When Romeo first sees Juliet, his sad mood suddenly changes. On page 77, Romeo describes Juliet's beauty. On the lines below, write two phrases that Romeo uses to describe Juliet. List the line number for each phrase in the column at the right. An example has been done for you.

Example:

"Oh, she teaches the torches to burn brightly!" _____ | line 44

a. _____
_____
_____

b. _____
_____
_____

Act I, Scene v

2. Read your responses to question 1. Which line do you think describes Juliet most clearly? Write the line below and explain your choice.

    _____

    _____

    _____

    _____

3. Capulet forbids Tybalt to fight with Romeo at the banquet. From Capulet's words, find two lines that show how he feels about Romeo. Write the lines below. Then list the page and line numbers for each phrase in the column at the right.

    a. _____

        _____

    b. _____

        _____

4. When Romeo and Juliet first meet, they refer to each other in religious terms. He speaks as though she is a _____ , and she calls him a _____ . In your own words, explain why they would speak to each other in such terms.

    page 81, lines 100–114

    _____

    _____

    _____

    _____

5. Describe Romeo's reaction when he learns that Juliet is a Capulet. Explain why he feels this way. _____

    page 83, lines 123–124

    _____

    _____

    _____

    _____

continued

Act I, Scene v

Reading Questions *Continued*	Pages/lines

6. What does Juliet say when she learns who Romeo is? Write her words and explain what she means. _____

_____

_____

_____

page 85,
lines 144–147

Response Log

Imagine how a first date that you might have would be different from Romeo and Juliet's first meeting. Pretend you are going out on a date for the first time with someone you really like. What are some places you might like to go? What special clothes would you wear? How would you talk and act?

First brainstorm about these questions with two or three other students. Then write your responses on the chart below. You may have several ideas in each category.

Share your responses with the class. Then be ready to discuss how modern dates differ from Romeo and Juliet's first meeting.

Where you'd go	What you'd wear	What you'd say	How you'd act

Discussion Questions

1. In the prologue, the chorus outlines the whole story for you. Do you like knowing the outcome of the play? Or would you prefer the ending to be a surprise? Explain your opinion.

2. How would you describe the personalities of Romeo and Juliet? Jot down three words or phrases that describe each character. Consider what Romeo and Juliet say and do as well as what other characters say about them. Be ready to discuss your answers.

   Romeo a. _____

            b. _____

            c. _____

   Juliet   a. _____

            b. _____

            c. _____

3. Romeo and Juliet are described as "ill-fated" lovers. What is the main obstacle that stands in the way of their love? If they asked you for advice, what would you suggest?

Act II, Prologue–Scene i

Pages 93–97

Setting the Stage

In the Middle Ages, people believed that falling in love could be dangerous. A person who fell in love too quickly and deeply might not be able to make wise decisions. A lover who was "hit by Cupid's arrow" would not be able to think or act sensibly.

As you read Scene i, observe how Mercutio describes the love-struck Romeo.

Reading Questions	**Pages/lines**

> The prologue at the beginning of Act II briefly reviews the major events in Act I. The lovers' terrible problems are contrasted with their sweet love.

1. Both Romeo and Juliet have been bewitched by _____ | page 93, line 6

_____

2. List two difficulties that the lovers face. Write the page and line numbers for your answers in the column at the right.
   a. _____

   _____

   b. _____

   _____

3. According to the chorus, what will help Romeo and Juliet overcome their problems? List two ideas in your answer. | page 93, lines 13–14
   a. _____

   _____

   b. _____

   _____

Act II, Prologue–Scene i

> At the beginning of Scene i, Benvolio and Mercutio are searching for Romeo. He hears their calls, but he doesn't answer. He is looking for Juliet.

4. Just before his friends call him, Romeo _____

_____

page 95,
stage directions

Act II, Prologue–Scene i

Response Log

Elizabethans had their own symbols and phrases of love. For example, Venus, Cupid, and King Cophetua are all symbols of love to Romeo and his friends. Notice, too, how Mercutio and Benvolio describe Romeo's feelings of love with phrases from their era. For example, Mercutio says Romeo "doesn't hear, he doesn't stir, he doesn't move."

Think of some modern symbols of love. List or draw these symbols below.

Then list some words or phrases from modern language that describe a person who is in love. It might help to think how love is described in popular songs.

Symbols of Love

Phrases of Love

Act II, Scene ii

Setting the Stage

Juliet, like other young women from wealthy families, has been carefully prepared for courtship and marriage. She has been trained to hide her real feelings. She also is expected to be shy and modest with men. Only men are allowed to be bold and outgoing during courtship.

However, in Scene ii, Juliet does not behave as she has been taught. Notice how her behavior is different from what is expected of young women.

Reading Questions   **Pages/lines**

> Scene ii, sometimes called the balcony scene, is very famous. Romeo secretly enters the Capulet orchard. Juliet comes out on her balcony alone. Romeo and Juliet then speak of their love for each other. Before the lovers part, they will say goodnight "a thousand times."

1. Shakespeare uses images of light and brightness to create certain feelings. Notice how Romeo uses these kinds of images when he talks to Juliet. Write three examples from page 99 in which Romeo compares Juliet's beauty to something that is light. List the line number for each example in the column at the right.

   a. _____

   _____

   _____

   b. _____

   _____

   _____

   c. _____

   _____

   _____

continued

Act II, Scene ii

Reading Questions *Continued* — **Pages/lines**

2. Reread the examples you gave in question 1. What mood or feelings do these words of light and brightness create for you?

_____

_____

_____

3. Juliet says that her enemy is not Romeo, but only his _____

page 101, line 40

_____

4. Romeo, who has been hiding in the orchard, calls out to Juliet. Juliet speaks to him from her balcony. She is worried about Romeo because _____

page 103, lines 68–74

_____

5. Juliet admits that her behavior towards Romeo is "immodest." Explain what Juliet does and says that embarrasses her. _____

pages 101–105

_____

_____

_____

_____

6. Juliet says to Romeo that she is "not delighted by our pledges tonight." In your own words, explain what she fears about their love. _____

page 107, lines 122–128

_____

_____

7. Juliet will send a messenger to Romeo tomorrow to find out

page 109, lines 149–152

_____

Act II, Scene ii

Response Log

Juliet says, "What's in a name? The thing which we call a rose would smell just as sweet if it had any other name.... Romeo, get rid of your name, and in place of that name, which isn't part of you, take me."

1. Is it only their names that separate Romeo and Juliet? If Romeo should change his name, do you think their problems would be solved? Explain your answer.

2. Are you satisfied with your name? Why or why not? If you could change your name, what would you choose? Why?

Act II, Scene iii

Setting the Stage

During the Middle Ages, priests and friars filled several roles. Men of the church ran schools and tutored wealthy children. They also helped both rich and poor people solve spiritual and personal problems. Sometimes priests and friars even served as matchmakers.

Some friars were also herbalists. These men used plants (herbs) to try to cure illnesses. They might also be asked to provide protection from diseases, injury in battle, or even mad dogs.

In Scene iii, you will see how the Friar serves as both an advisor and a healer. Notice how he uses his knowledge of nature as he gives advice to Romeo.

Reading Questions	**Pages/lines**

> It is dawn. Friar Lawrence is at the church. Much to his surprise, young Romeo comes to him at this early hour.

1. The Friar is collecting "deadly weeds and healing flowers." As he does this, he compares earth to a _____ and the plants to her _____ . Explain why the earth and plants could be described in this way. _____

   _____

   _____

   _____

page 115, lines 9–12

Act II, Scene iii

2. Complete the Friar's speech that he says as he holds up a flower.

page 115, lines 23–26

> Within the new bud of this weak _____ , there
>   lies _____ and medicinal power.
> If you smell this flower, you'll be _____
>   all over; but if you _____ this flower, you die.

What is the Friar saying about the powers of natural plants and herbs? _____

page 115, lines 9–26

_____

_____

3. The Friar gives the same warning about humans. The two "opposed kings" that "always live within man, as well as in herbs" are _____ and _____ . The Friar is saying that humans can be both _____ and

page 115, lines 27–28

_____ .

4. Romeo asks the Friar to _____

page 119, lines 64–65

5. Friar Lawrence disapproves of Romeo's behavior. Explain why he scolds Romeo. _____

pages 119–121, lines 66–91

_____

_____

_____

_____

6. Even though the Friar is upset, he agrees to Romeo's request for one reason. He hopes that _____

page 121, lines 94–95

_____

Act II, Scene iii

Response Log

The Friar warns Romeo that good things—including people—also have the power to cause evil.

In the chart below, list the good and bad qualities (strengths and weaknesses) of three people. List at least one strength and one weakness for each person.

Two of the people you describe should be characters from the play (such as Romeo, Juliet, the Nurse). For the third person, choose anyone you wish. You could choose a historical figure, fictional character, TV or movie personality, or yourself.

An example has been done for you.

Person	Strengths	Weaknesses
Example: Lady Montague	loving mother	sometimes inconsiderate of others' feelings
	kind to those who work for her	too concerned with wealth and social position
1.		
2.		
3.		

Act II, Scene iv

Setting the Stage

Upper-class women in Verona were treated with courtesy. They were praised in poetry and love ballads.

Lower-class women, however, did not get this respect. Men often used vulgar language when speaking to them. The lower-class women were simply expected to accept such harsh treatment.

In Scene iv, Benvolio, Mercutio, and Romeo meet Juliet's nurse. As you read, notice how Romeo and his friends treat the Nurse.

Reading Questions	Pages/lines

> Mercutio and Benvolio are still searching the streets of Verona. They cannot find Romeo. He hasn't been seen since Capulet's party.

1. Tybalt has sent a letter to Romeo. Mercutio believes that the letter contains _____

page 123, line 8

continued

Act II, Scene iv

Reading Questions *Continued*	Pages/lines

2. On pages 131–135, find two examples of how Benvolio and Mercutio are rude to the Nurse. On the lines below, first write the speaker's name and what he says. Record the page and line numbers for each phrase in the column at the right. Then explain what the speaker means. An example has been done for you.

Example:

Romeo: "A sail, a sail!" Romeo means that the Nurse is a

large woman.

page 131, line 89

a. _____

_____

_____

b. _____

_____

_____

3. What two instructions does Romeo give the Nurse?

pages 137–139,
lines 158–169

a. _____

_____

_____

b. _____

_____

_____

Act II, Scene iv

Response Log

Benvolio and Mercutio mistreat the Nurse because she is a woman in a lower social class. Think about how people today are treated unfairly because they belong to a certain group.

Below are listed five ways people can be grouped. With a partner, write down examples of how people are viewed or mistreated because *they belong to a certain part of that group.* You may use first-hand experiences, incidents you have read about, or something you have seen on TV or in the movies.

Try to give at least one example for each group. An example has been done for you.

Group	Unfair Treatment
1. social class	a. *Example:* lower-class people are sometimes considered lazy
	b.
2. sex (male or female)	a.
	b.
3. age	a.
	b.
4. race or ethnic group	a.
	b.
5. neighborhood	a.
	b.

Act II, Scenes v–vi

Pages 143–151

Setting the Stage

Today a couple can be legally married without a religious ceremony. However, in the Middle Ages only marriages performed by a clergyman were legal.

A wedding was a joyous event that was celebrated by many friends and relatives. After the ceremony, the guests followed the couple through the streets to the home of the bride or groom. Then a wedding feast was held that lasted into the night. Notice how different Juliet's wedding is from a typical ceremony of the day.

Reading Questions | **Pages/lines**

> Scene v opens at noon in the Capulet orchard. Juliet is waiting for her nurse to return with a message from Romeo. The Nurse has been gone three hours, and Juliet is getting worried.

1. Juliet begs the Nurse to report what Romeo said. As the Nurse rambles on and complains of her hard day, she also speaks of Romeo's good traits. List three of Romeo's qualities that the Nurse admires.

    pages 145–147, lines 39–57

    a. _____

    b. _____

    c. _____

> In Scene vi, Romeo and Juliet come to Friar Lawrence's cell to be married.

2. On page 149, lines 6–8, Romeo's words show how much he loves Juliet. He is willing to risk _____ in order to

    _____.

Act II, Scenes v–vi

3. Friar Lawrence gives Romeo more advice. Complete the Friar's words.

page 149, lines 9–15

Violent _____ have violent ends,
and in triumph they _____ , like fire and
    gunpowder . . . .
So love _____ . Love that _____
    a long time is moderate.
To push love too _____ can be as bad as being
    too _____ to love.

With these words, the Friar warns Romeo that _____

_____

_____

Act II, Scenes v–vi

Response Log

Before the Friar marries Romeo to Juliet, he warns Romeo that "violent passions have violent ends."

On the chart below, list four normal human emotions or desires. (You might consider such feelings as love, anger, happiness, loneliness, or acceptance.) Then give at least two examples to describe what can happen when each feeling you listed grows too strong.

After you complete the chart, compare your responses with a classmate's. An example has been done for you.

Emotion or Desire	Dangers
Example: 　ambition	a. may lose friends and loved ones b. may become too concerned with money and power
1.	a. b.
2.	a. b.
3.	a. b.
4.	a. b.

Act II

Discussion Questions

1. In Act II, the Friar scolds Romeo for changing his mind so quickly. Romeo claimed he was in love with Rosaline. Now he wants to marry Juliet. The Friar tells Romeo, "Young men's love lies not in their hearts but in their eyes." What does the Friar mean?

   Do you think the Friar is right and Romeo's love lies only in his eyes? What is your opinion of Juliet? Does she love Romeo with her heart or her eyes? Explain your answer.

2. The reader gets to know the Nurse better in Act II. What do you like or dislike about the Nurse? How would the story be different if she weren't in it?

3. Compare Juliet's relationship with her nurse to her relationship with her mother. Does Juliet seem closer to one woman than the other? Does she act differently around each one? Explain your responses and support your answers with evidence from the play.

continued

Discussion Questions *Continued*

---

4. Have you ever heard the saying "throw caution to the wind"?
    That phrase can be used to explain what Romeo and Juliet have
    done. They have let their emotions guide their actions without
    thinking about the consequences or results.

      Map all the consequences that might result from Romeo and
    Juliet's actions. Think of both good and bad results. After your
    list is complete, be ready to discuss your ideas.

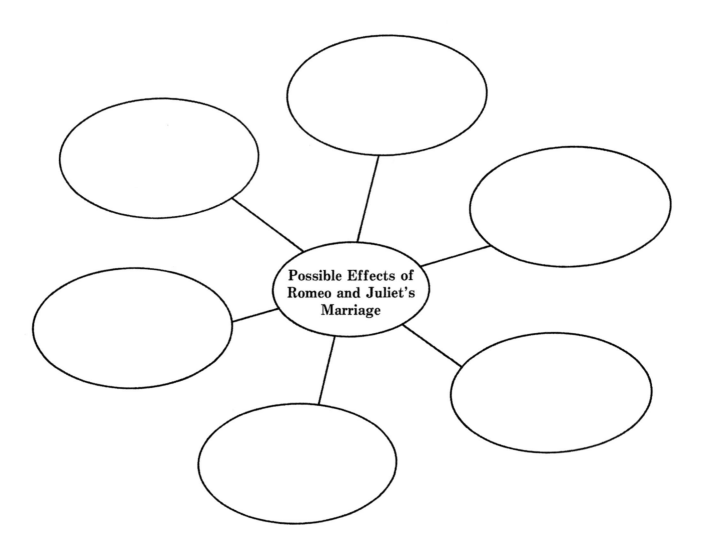

Possible Effects of Romeo and Juliet's Marriage

Act III, Scene i

Setting the Stage

A young man of the upper class was given great freedom in Elizabethan time. Unlike a young woman, he could spend time with his friends without chaperones. He and his friends were allowed to drink in taverns, go horseback racing, hunt, box, and play tennis. On rainy days, they might gamble on a game of cards or dice.

During their time together, young men also had the chance to share their problems. As a result, they often developed close friendships.

In Scene i, observe the devotion Romeo and his friends have for each other. Romeo's friends worry about him and defend his honor. Romeo even kills another person to avenge a friend.

Reading Questions   **Pages/lines**

> It is broad daylight in Verona. Mercutio and Benvolio are on the street. Their conversation shows that the feud is becoming as hot as the weather.

1. When he meets Benvolio and Mercutio, Tybalt is looking for

   _____

   page 161,
   line 41

2. How does Mercutio treat Tybalt when they meet? Circle the best answer.

   a. Mercutio ignores Tybalt.
   b. Mercutio tries to be polite and civil.
   c. Mercutio insults Tybalt and tries to get him angry.
   d. Mercutio is angry but holds his tongue.

   pages 161–163,
   lines 32–51

3. Why does Romeo refuse to fight Tybalt? _____

   _____

   _____

   _____

   _____

   pages 163,
   lines 58–68

continued

Act III, Scene i

Reading Questions *Continued*	**Pages/lines**

4. Explain what happens when Romeo tries to stop the fight. _____

   _____

   _____

   _____

   _____

pages 165–167, lines 81–95

5. After Mercutio is wounded, he twice cries out, "A curse on both your houses!"

   a. Who are the people Mercutio is cursing? _____

      _____

   b. What does Mercutio mean when he curses both their houses?

      _____

      _____

      _____

pages 165–167, lines 87, 95–96

6. Why does the Prince announce that he has "a personal interest in this fight"? _____

   _____

   _____

   _____

   _____

page 173, lines 187–198

7. The Prince sets Romeo's punishment. Romeo must _____
   _____ or _____ within the hour.

page 173, lines 195–196

Act III, Scene i

Response Log

Mercutio is killed when Romeo tries to stop the fight. If Romeo had not become involved, Mercutio might not have died.

Think of a time when you tried to help a friend (or a friend tried to help you), but the situation only got worse. First explain the conflict. Then tell why you (or your friend) became involved and what you would do differently if you could.

Act III, Scene ii

Pages 175–183

Setting the Stage

Tales of Greek and Roman myths were often told to youngsters in ages past. Juliet, too, seems to know these stories. As she waits alone for her nurse, she wishes that a "driver like Phaeton" would chase the sun from the sky. Then Romeo could come to her.

Phaeton was the son of Phoebus, the Greek sun god. Phoebus had a chariot of fire, which Phaeton borrowed one day to speed through the heavens. But Phaeton drove carelessly and lost control of the horses. As a result, the chariot flew too near the earth, and several mountain ranges were set on fire.

Zeus, the ruler of the gods, saw the destruction caused by the blazing chariot. To save the world, Zeus struck down the chariot. Phaeton died as the chariot plunged to the ground.

The tale of Phaeton and Phoebus teaches that death can result from youthful passion and impatience. As you read Scene ii, think of how this lesson has come true for the two young lovers.

Act III, Scene ii

Reading Questions	Pages/lines

> Juliet is again waiting for her nurse. She knows nothing of the two deaths. She is only thinking about the arrival of her new husband.

1. When Juliet learns that Romeo has killed Tybalt, she cries, "Oh, how can he hide such an evil heart with such a beautiful face?" Juliet is saying that there are opposites in Romeo's nature. Find three other examples where Juliet says that Romeo is not what he appears to be. List the line numbers for each phrase in the column at the right.

   pages 179–181, lines 75–87

   a. _____

   _____

   b. _____

   _____

   c. _____

   _____

2. Juliet says, "There was a word, worse than Tybalt's death, that murdered me." The word she fears is _____ . To Juliet the word means that _____

   _____

   pages 181–183, lines 112–131

3. The Nurse tries to comfort Juliet by making a promise. Which of the following promises does she make to Juliet? Circle the letter of the best answer.

   page 183, lines 142–145

   a. She will always defend the murderer Romeo.
   b. She will find Romeo and bring him to Juliet.
   c. She will tell Juliet's parents that Romeo is their son-in-law and they should forgive him.
   d. She will help Juliet to run away with Romeo.

Act III, Scene ii

Response Log

In an ancient Greek myth, the young and impatient Phaeton ignored his father's warning. As he searched for adventure, he brought about his own death.

Write about a similar incident. Describe how a young person you know got into trouble in search of adventure. In your description, explain the rules or warnings the person ignored.

Act III, Scene iii

Setting the Stage

Romeo says, "To be banished from Verona is to be banished from the world." Why would banishment be such a terrible punishment?

In the Middle Ages, the city seemed like the entire world to its citizens. A city was similar to an independent state. It had its own ruler, laws, and army.

The ruler of a city had great power. He could even decide how a criminal would be punished. One of the worst punishments was to banish or exile a person from the city. A banished person would no longer have the protection of the city. The exiled person might have to wander alone in a dangerous world of wars, bandits, bad roads, and diseases. For some people, banishment was worse than death.

In Scene iii, observe how Romeo reacts when he learns that he must leave Verona and his beloved Juliet.

Reading Questions	**Pages/lines**

Romeo is hiding in Friar Lawrence's cell. He is waiting to hear of his punishment for killing Tybalt.

1. Check all the words that describe Romeo's mood as he reacts to the news of his punishment.

    _____ a. angry   _____ e. prayerful

    _____ b. regretful   _____ f. stubborn

    _____ c. suicidal   _____ g. controlled

    _____ d. hopeful   _____ h. uncontrolled

    pages 185–193, lines 1–111

2. Explain how the Nurse saves Romeo. _____

    _____

    _____

    page 193, lines 110–111; stage directions

continued

Reading Questions *Continued*	Pages/lines

3. According to the Friar, what does Romeo have to be thankful for? List three ways Romeo is fortunate.

   a. _____

   b. _____

   c. _____

page 195,
lines 139–144

4. The Friar tries to give Romeo courage and hope by advising him to do three things. List the Friar's advice to Romeo.

   a. _____

   _____

   b. _____

   _____

   c. _____

   _____

page 195,
lines 150–162

Act III, Scene iii

Response Log

At this point in the story, you may have questions for some of the characters. You may want to ask why they did something or why they didn't do something. Perhaps you would like to make a suggestion to a character. Or maybe you feel a character should be praised or scolded. This is your chance to talk to the characters.

a. Think of two or three characters that you would like to talk to. Write their names in the *a* spaces below.

b. Think of a question or suggestion for each character you have listed. Write the questions or suggestions in the *b* spaces below.

c. Trade your Response Log with another student. Pretend you are the character being spoken to. Then respond to your partner's questions or comments in the *c* spaces below. Try to respond the way you think that character would.

1. a. **Character:**
    b. **Question or comment:**
    c. **Response:**

2. a. **Character:**
    b. **Question or comment:**
    c. **Response:**

3. a. **Character:**
    b. **Question or comment:**
    c. **Response:**

Act III, Scenes iv–v

Setting the Stage

When a father chose a husband for his daughter in the Middle Ages, wealth came before love. A father wanted to find a rich husband who could provide for his daughter. The bridegroom also had to be from the same social class as the woman. It was important that a woman never marry a man from a lower social class. Romantic love was rarely the reason for two people to marry.

A father expected his daughter to accept the man he chose for her husband. As you read Scenes iv and v, think about the risks Juliet is taking as she defies her father.

Reading Questions	**Pages/lines**

Earlier, Paris asked Lord Capulet for Juliet's hand in marriage. In Scene iv, he comes to the Capulet home to speak to her parents again. He finds the Capulets in mourning for their beloved nephew Tybalt.

1. In Act I, Lord Capulet said that Paris had to win Juliet's consent to marry. Why then does Capulet now agree to Paris' request without Juliet's approval? _____

   _____

   _____

   _____

   page 199, lines 12–16

2. This day is Monday. Paris will wed Juliet on _____

   page 201, line 31

Scene v begins early Tuesday morning. This should be a happy time for Romeo and Juliet since they are together. But Romeo must leave for Mantua before dawn.

Act III, Scenes iv–v

3. Juliet says to Romeo, "It was the nightingale, not the lark, that sang in your apprehensive ear . . . . Believe me, love, it was the nightingale." Explain why Romeo and Juliet would rather hear the nightingale sing than the lark. _____

_____

_____

_____

pages 203–205, lines 1–36

4. As Romeo leaves, Juliet has a feeling of doom. What does Juliet see that frightens her? _____

_____

page 207, lines 54–57

5. Lady Capulet tells Juliet that in order to get revenge for Tybalt's death, she will _____

_____

_____

page 209, lines 91–96

6. When Juliet says that she will not marry Paris, her father reacts violently. Circle the reaction or remark Lord Capulet does *not* make as he scolds Juliet.

a. Juliet is an ungrateful daughter.
b. If Juliet disobeys him, she can die in the streets.
c. He'd like to hit her.
d. He will have Romeo killed.
e. He and his wife have been cursed by having Juliet as their child.

pages 215–217, lines 165–205

7. What advice does the Nurse give Juliet? _____

_____

_____

page 219, lines 223–236

continued

© Perfection Learning® No reproduction permitted.

Romeo and Juliet • Act III, Scenes iv–v 45

Reading Questions *Continued*	Pages/lines

8. After hearing the Nurse's advice, Juliet says, "You and my real feelings are separated now forever." Explain what Juliet means.

page 221, line 251

_____

_____

_____

9. What does Juliet decide to do?_____

page 221, lines 252–253

_____

_____

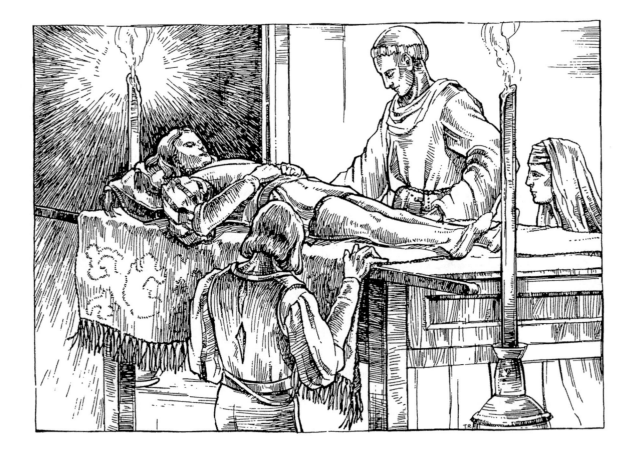

Act III, Scenes iv–v

Response Log

Juliet challenges her father's authority. She argues with him and
begs him, but he will not listen to her. In turn, he threatens her.
However, she will not change her mind. Neither person listens to
the other in this conflict.

   Pretend you are Juliet. What could you say to change your
parents' minds? Complete this dialogue between father and
daughter. Try to get your father to understand your feelings.

Lord Capulet:
   If you don't marry, you can hang, beg, starve, and
      die in the streets,
   for I swear, I'll never recognize you
   as my daughter again.
   And I'll never give you anything.
   Count on that! Think about it. I won't go back on
      my word.

Juliet:

Lord Capulet:

Juliet:

Lord Capulet:

Juliet:

Act III

Discussion Questions

1. In Act II, Scene ii, Shakespeare uses light and brightness to create feelings of happiness and love. However, the images of light and dawn in Act III have a different meaning. Reread pages 203–205 in Act III, Scene v. What do dawn and light mean to Romeo and Juliet here?

2. Both Romeo and Juliet speak of the power of fate. After killing Tybalt, Romeo says, "I'm a victim of fate" (page 169). And when Romeo leaves for Mantua, Juliet asks Fate to return Romeo to her (page 207).

    In what ways do you think fate is responsible for Romeo and Juliet's problems? In what ways are Romeo and Juliet responsible for their own problems?

Act III

3. Both Romeo and Juliet make remarks that hint of tragic events in the future. These hints are called *foreshadowing*. Reread pages 169, 179, and 207. Find lines that hint of possible danger. (You may want to write the lines and the speaker below.) What kind of mood or feeling do these lines create for the reader? What do you think these hints mean?

Act IV, Scene i

Setting the Stage

In Act II, Scene iii, the Friar looked to herbs and plants to explain the good and evil in all human beings. In Act IV, Scene i, Friar Lawrence once again uses his knowledge of nature as he tries to help Romeo and Juliet. Now the Friar will use natural elements to create a drug for Juliet.

The potion the Friar mixes is an element of fantasy in the play. No drug has ever existed, even today, that is exactly like the Friar's potion. As you read this scene, think about the dangers in the Friar's solution to Romeo and Juliet's problems.

Reading Questions	**Pages/lines**

This scene takes place in Friar Lawrence's cell. Paris has come to tell the Friar of the wedding. Shortly after Paris arrives, Juliet also appears unexpectedly to talk to the Friar. Imagine her tension at this meeting where she must hide her real feelings from Paris

1. The Friar tells Paris that there is one thing about the marriage plans that he doesn't like. Circle the letter of the statement that best describes what the Friar tells Paris.

    a. Juliet will be married to two men.
    b. Paris doesn't know how Juliet feels about the marriage.
    c. Juliet doesn't love Paris.
    d. It is too soon after Tybalt's death for Juliet to marry.

    page 229, lines 4–5

2. Juliet tells the Friar that if he can't help her, she will _____

    _____

    page 233, lines 55–61

3. Explain the Friar's unusual plan by completing the list below.
    a. On Wednesday night, Juliet will go to her room alone and will

    _____

    b. Immediately, Juliet will _____

    _____

    pages 235–237, lines 91–122

Act IV, Scene i

   c. Thursday morning, Paris will _____

      _____

   d. Then Juliet's family will _____

      _____

   e. To let Romeo know of Juliet's condition, the Friar will _____

      _____

   f. Finally, Romeo will _____

      _____

Act IV, Scene i

Response Log

So far in the play, we have heard several opinions about how Romeo and Juliet should solve their problem. The Nurse tells Juliet to forget Romeo and marry Paris. The Friar invents a risky plan that requires Juliet to be buried alive. And Juliet threatens to commit suicide if the Friar can't help her.

Explain your reaction to each plan. Then tell what *you* think Romeo and Juliet should do to solve their problem.

1. **Reaction to the Nurse's plan:**

2. **Reaction to the Friar's plan:**

3. **Reaction to Juliet's plan:**

4. **Your plan:**

Act IV, Scenes ii–iii

Setting the Stage

During the Middle Ages, burial practices differed for people in the upper and lower classes. Poor people were usually buried in simple graves. But the bodies of wealthy people were often placed in a family tomb or vault. These huge stone structures were built above ground. They were dark and damp places, filled with ancient bones and sealed with boulders to keep out intruders and robbers.

As you read Scene iii, imagine what it would be like to awaken alone in such a tomb.

Act IV, Scenes ii–iii

Reading Questions	Pages/lines

Scene ii begins on Tuesday night. As Juliet's parents are making preparations for her wedding, she knocks on their door. She speaks to her parents as a respectful and obedient daughter.

1. What does Juliet ask of her parents? _____

page 241, lines 20–21

_____

2. How does Juliet explain her change in attitude to her parents?

page 241, lines 16–20

_____

Scene iii takes place in Juliet's bedroom later that night. Juliet convinces her mother and the Nurse to leave her so she can pray. But what she actually does when they depart is prepare to drink the Friar's potion.

3. List three fears that Juliet has about the Friar's dangerous plan. Write the page and line numbers for your answers in the column at the right. An example has been done for you.

Example:

The mixture will not work, and Juliet will have to marry

page 245, lines 22–23

Paris.

a. _____

_____

b. _____

_____

c. _____

Act IV, Scenes ii–iii

Pages 239–247

Response Log

To Juliet, being alone in a dark cemetery is a terrifying thought. Images of cemeteries and tombstones still frighten many people today.

   With a partner, create a description of a cemetery at night. First list words and phrases that show how the scene looks, sounds—even how it smells and feels. You can explain both physical and emotional feelings. Write the words and phrases in the columns below. Use your imagination!

   Then with your partner write a one-paragraph description of the cemetery. Include the descriptive words and phrases that you both think are the most vivid. Be ready to share your description with the class.

Sights	Sounds	Smells	Feelings

Description of cemetery:

Act IV, Scenes iv–v

Pages 249–263

Setting the Stage

Death was not a stranger to people in the Middle Ages. Men and women rarely lived beyond their early forties. Disease, childbirth, and war all took their toll. To faithful Christians, however, death was both an ending and a beginning. Even though they knew life on earth would end, true believers felt they would begin a new life in God's kingdom.

In Scene v, notice what the Friar says to comfort the grieving Capulets.

Reading Questions	**Pages/lines**

> The night before the wedding, the Capulets stay up late to prepare for the banquet.

1. In Scene iv, the reader gets a hint about Lord and Lady Capulet's marriage. According to Lady Capulet, why had Lord Capulet stayed up late in the past? _____

   _____

   _____

page 249, lines 10–13

> Wednesday morning, the Nurse is sent to awaken the bride. To her horror, she discovers Juliet lying on the bed, apparently dead.

2. When Capulet learns of his daughter's death, he is grief-stricken. He compares death to an _____ that lies on Juliet, the _____ Explain why death and Juliet can be described in this manner.

   _____

   _____

page 255, lines 30–31

Act IV, Scenes iv–v

3. What does the Friar tell the mourners in order to comfort them?

pages 257–259,
lines 68–86

_____

_____

_____

_____

4. Friar Lawrence and Capulet speak of preparation for Juliet's funeral. List the things the family will do to prepare for her burial.

page 259,
lines 82–93

a. _____

b. _____

c. _____

d. _____

Act IV, Scenes iv–v

Response Log

The Capulets prepare for two important ceremonies—first a wedding, then a funeral. Their emotions swiftly change from joy to sorrow.

Describe either a wedding or a funeral that you have attended or seen in a movie or on TV. Then compare and contrast the event with the same ceremony in the Middle Ages. There is no actual wedding or funeral in the play. So you must base your ideas on how the Capulets prepare for each ceremony. You might also get information in the library about these Elizabethan ceremonies.

Use the chart on page 59 to list as many likenesses and differences as you can. You don't need to have the same number of ideas in each column.

Description of a modern wedding or funeral:

Description of an Elizabethan wedding or funeral:

Act IV, Scenes iv–v

Pages 249–263

Likenesses	Differences
1.	1.
2.	2.
3.	3.
4.	4.
5.	5.

1. Discuss the Friar's motives for his unusual plan to help the two lovers. What suggests he truly cares about Romeo and Juliet and is trying to unite their families? What suggests that he might have other motives?

2. Juliet apologizes to her parents for her rude and rebellious behavior. Do you think her apology is just an act, or is it possible that she is sincere? Explain your answer.

Act IV

3. The audience learns a lot about the character of Juliet in Act IV. How has Juliet changed since the beginning of the play? What do you think of her feelings for Romeo now? Does she love him with her heart or just her eyes? Give examples to support your answer.

Act V, Scene i

Setting the Stage

In this scene, Romeo goes to find a pharmacist. In the Middle Ages (as today), a pharmacist mixed drugs to prevent and cure illnesses. Since some of these drugs were poisonous, a pharmacist had to follow strict laws in many city-states. Notice how Romeo is able to persuade the pharmacist to break the law and sell him a poisonous powder.

Reading Questions	**Pages/lines**

> Juliet has been buried in the Capulet tomb. Among those who attended her funeral was Balthasar, Romeo's page. Now Balthasar has come to Mantua to tell Romeo that Juliet is dead.

1. As Romeo awaits Balthasar, he remembers a dream he had.

   a. Describe Romeo's dream. _____

   _____

   b. Explain what you think his dream means. _____

   _____

   _____

   _____

   page 271, lines 6–11

2. Romeo reacts strongly when he hears that Juliet is dead. What does Balthasar fear that Romeo will do? _____

   _____

   _____

   page 271, lines 27–29

3. Why does Romeo believe that the pharmacist will sell poison to him? _____

   _____

   _____

   page 273, lines 39–57

Act V, Scene i

Response Log

Once again, Romeo makes a quick decision. When he hears of Juliet's death, he reacts before he considers all the possible results. Most people have done this sometime in their life.

Write about a time when you acted like Romeo and made a decision without thinking. First explain what you did and what happened as a result of your action. Then, based on your experience, give Romeo two or three sentences of advice about making decisions.

Act V, Scenes ii–iii

Setting the Stage

During the 1300s, waves of fast-spreading, deadly diseases (called plagues) swept across Europe. The most frightening plague in history was the Black Plague. In three years, at least 25 million people (one-fourth of Europe's population) died from the disease. The only way to stop the spread of a plague was to isolate (quarantine) the victims. This meant that no one would be allowed to enter or leave an area where there were infected people.

In Scene ii, notice how a plague affects the fates of Romeo and Juliet.

Reading Questions	**Pages/lines**

> In Scene ii, Friar John returns to Verona to tell Friar Lawrence that he was not able to give the letter to Romeo.

1. Explain why Friar John could not get to Mantua. _____

_____

_____

_____

page 277,
lines 5–12

> Scene iii opens at night in the churchyard where the Capulet tomb is located. Paris has come with flowers for Juliet's grave. Then Romeo also appears, ready to carry out his dreadful plan.

Act V, Scenes ii–iii

2. Before Romeo enters the tomb, he speaks the following lines. Fill in the blanks with the correct words.

page 283, lines 45–48

You detestable _____ . You womb of _____ .
You are gorged with the dearest morsel on _____ . So
I'll force your rotten _____ to open, and to spite you,
I'll _____ you with more _____ !

   a. What do you think Romeo is describing? _____

   _____

   b. Explain the comparison Romeo is making. _____

   _____

   _____

   _____

   _____

   _____

3. Explain what happens when Paris tries to arrest Romeo. _____

page 285, lines 56–73

   _____

   _____

   _____

4. Romeo says to Paris, "Good gentle youth, don't tempt a desperate man . . . . don't lay another sin on my head . . . . later you can say that a madman's mercy told you to run away." According to Romeo's words, how does he feel about himself at this point in the story? Write your answer on the lines below.

page 285, lines 59–67

   _____

   _____

   _____

   _____

continued

Reading Questions *Continued*

Pages/lines

5. Whom or what does Romeo blame for all the terrible events that have occured since he fell in love with Juliet? (Hint: The answer is mentioned twice.) _____

pages 287–289,
lines 82 and 111

_____

6. Friar Lawrence enters the tomb and finds the bodies of Paris and Romeo. As Juliet awakens, he pleads with her to _____

page 293,
lines 159–164

_____

7. Instead of doing what the Friar wishes, Juliet _____

page 293,
lines 165–176

_____

8. Friar Lawrence reveals all that has happened to the lovers and how he is involved. List the characters that are present to hear his confession.

pages 299–301,
lines 235–275

_____

_____

9. Why is Lady Montague not present? _____

page 297,
lines 216–217

_____

10. The Prince says, "We've all been punished." Explain whom he means by "we" and how these people have been punished.

page 303,
lines 295–301

_____

_____

_____

11. What will the two fathers do to honor Romeo and Juliet? _____

page 303,
lines 305–311

_____

Act V, Scenes ii–iii

Response Log

By now the Prince knows all the events that led to the tragic
deaths of five young people. It is his job to decide the fates of the
people involved. He says some people will be pardoned and some
will be punished.

   Put yourself in the Prince's role. First decide which characters are
in any way responsible for the tragedy. You should consider
characters who are dead as well as living at the end of the play.
List the characters and their actions (offenses) that helped cause the
tragedy.

   Then explain how you will sentence each person. Should the
offender be punished or pardoned? If the person is dead by the end
of the play, leave the last column blank.

	Character	Offense	Punishment
1.			
2.			
3.			
4.			
5.			
6.			

Romeo and Juliet •

Discussion Questions

---

1. Read Romeo's comments on page 287, lines 74–101. Explain how his words show that he has changed since he met Juliet. Consider what Romeo has discovered about himself and others.

2. The audience learns in the prologue that the play will end with the deaths of Romeo and Juliet. Suppose you didn't know this before you read the play. Do you think you would be surprised at the ending? Would you like this story better if it had a happy ending? Defend your opinion with specifics from the story.

3. The story of Romeo and Juliet is based on several key ideas (themes). Read the list of key ideas below. Then choose one of them you would like to discuss. Be ready to explain what you learned about the topic from the play. Use evidence from the play to explain your ideas.

   a. the power of love
   b. the importance of acting with caution and reason
   c. the effects of fate or chance
   d. the effects of prejudice and bigotry

4. Shakespeare borrowed the story of Romeo and Juliet from earlier writers. So the story of two lovers separated by their families' hatred is thousands of years old. Why do you think the story has appealed to people for this long? What can people learn from this play that is true no matter when or where they live?

Action Chart

Many characters in *Romeo and Juliet* believe that their actions are controlled by fortune or fate. Therefore, they feel they have little control over what they do and what happens to them.

This way of thinking is based on ancient belief. The Greeks believed fate was controlled by the goddess Fortune. The goddess decided a person's fate by spinning a huge wheel. The person's luck depended on where the wheel stopped.

In this exercise, you will discuss what caused an event or action. First, read the event in the column labeled **Effect**. Then think about what caused that event. The cause may be fate or chance, which means no one could have done anything to prevent the outcome. Or the cause may be a character's actions or beliefs.

Finally, in the column labeled **Cause**, explain what you think caused each event. An example has been done for you. (The example has two possible causes. You only need to give one cause for each event.)

Cause	Effect
Example: This event happened because of Romeo's actions. He chose to go to the banquet even though he knew it was dangerous. (Or, fate caused the two young people to fall in love. They had no control over their feelings.)	Romeo goes to the banquet and falls in love with the daughter of his enemy.
1. _____ _____ _____	1. Romeo and Juliet marry secretly instead of asking their parents' permission.

Cause	Effect
2. _____ _____ _____	2. Mercutio is killed.
3. _____ _____ _____	3. Romeo kills Tybalt.
4. _____ _____ _____	4. Lord Capulet agrees to let Paris marry Juliet.
5. _____ _____ _____	5. Juliet drinks the potion.
6. _____ _____ _____	6. Friar John never arrives at Mantua with the important letter.
7. _____ _____ _____	7. Romeo kills Paris.

continued

Cause	Effect
8. _____ _____ _____	8. Romeo drinks the poison.
9. _____ _____ _____	9. Juliet stabs herself.
10. _____ _____ _____	10. Friar Lawrence arrives too late to save Romeo and Juliet.

Extension Activities

1. The story of young lovers who are kept apart because of misunderstandings or prejudice is an old one. Shakespeare used this ancient tale as the basis for *Romeo and Juliet*.

   Find a modern story with a theme that is similar to *Romeo and Juliet*. The story could be from a movie, TV show, novel, short story, or song. Compare and contrast the plot, setting, and characters of this story to *Romeo and Juliet*. Write your findings in two or three paragraphs.

2. Arrange a trial for Friar Lawrence. Imagine that he is accused by the Capulet and Montague families of causing the deaths of their children. Select classsmates to portray the jury, judge, lawyers, and witnesses.

   Before the courtroom drama takes place, participants should prepare for their roles in the trial. Give each participant a brief outline of his or her character and role in the trial. This outline should explain what will happen in the trail. It will tell where each person will sit, the order in which the characters will speak, and so forth. It will also explain the characters' involvement in the tragic events.

3. Write Friar Lawrence's letter to Romeo. Describe the plan to help Romeo and Juliet as the Friar would have written it.

4. Write Romeo's letter, which was delivered to Lord Montague after his son's death. As Romeo, explain the events which led you to Juliet's grave and caused your death.

5. A casting director is responsible for selecting the right person to portray each character in a play or movie. Choosing the right actor is a complicated process. It involves finding a person with the right age, personality, looks, speech patterns—even gestures and voice.

   Imagine that you are selecting characters for *Romeo and Juliet*. Choose two modern-day actors to portray the lovers. Explain why the actors fit the characters in the play.

   You may prepare a poster or chart with pictures of the actors. Then on this chart, list the traits shared by the actors and the characters in the play.

continued

Extension Activities *continued*

6. Does the ending of *Romeo and Juliet* leave you unhappy and frustrated? Invent a new conclusion to the play which suits you. Go back into the play as far as necessary to create a different ending. Write your new ending in dialogue form.

7. Choose one dramatic scene in Shakespeare's play to rewrite in short story form. For instance, you might choose the fight between Mercutio and Tybalt, or the moment when Juliet's father informs her that she is to be married to Paris. Supply descriptive detail about the setting, characters, and action. Add excitement by using action verbs in your sentences. Be sure to use correct dialogue form in your story.

8. Write a report about one of the topics listed below. The information for your report should be limited to the late Middle Ages, from the 1300s to the 1500s. Use at least three resources, only one of which may be an encyclopedia. The report should be about two pages long.
   a. marriage customs
   b. education of upper-class children
   c. the Black Plague
   d. Shakespeare's Globe Theater
   e. superstitious beliefs
   f. clothing of the common people, nobles, and clergy
   g. medicine, science, astrology, and astronomy
   h. music and musical instruments

9. Select your favorite character in *Romeo and Juliet*. Examine his or her personality in a character sketch. Your written sketch will answer questions such as the following:
   - What do you learn about the character from his or her remarks, decisions, or behavior?
   - Does the character's behavior under stress show him or her to be mature or childish?
   - What are the character's relationships with other people like?
   - Is the character selfish or loving?
   - What is your opinion of this character?

   Use evidence from the play to support your ideas. The character sketch should be at least three paragraphs.

10. Many composers have been inspired by the story of Romeo and Juliet. For example, Tchaikovsky, Berlioz, and Gounod wrote music based on Shakespeare's play. Leonard Bernstein, a modern composer, wrote the score for *West Side Story*, an updated version of the play.

    Find at least two musical pieces based on *Romeo and Juliet*. In an oral presentation to your group or class, explain how the music matches the events and mood of the play. Explain the feelings and emotions the music creates for the listener. If possible, arrange to play some of the music for your classmates.

11. *Romeo and Juliet* tells the story of two young people from the moment they first see each other until the day they both die. Make a timeline which extends from Sunday, when the two Capulet men come on stage, until Friday, when Paris and Romeo come to Juliet's tomb. Write the important events from the play on the timeline. You may use use symbols or signs to make your timeline more interesting. Be sure to make a key for any symbols or signs you use on the timeline.

12. Create a playbill (program booklet) for *Romeo and Juliet* which might be given to a modern audience. Design a cover page for the booklet. On the inside, list the actors that play each character. You may choose real people or make up names. A playbill also lists the scenes with a brief description of the setting and action in each one. You could even include some advertising in your playbill. (It might be helpful if you got an example from your local theater or playhouse.)

13. Design costumes for the actors. Check a library for information on the kind of clothing worn by men and women during the 1300s in Italy. From authentic sketches and descriptions, draw models of dress during that period. You can make illustrations or even paper doll replicas of people in different costumes.

Writing Activities

1. Imagine you are a reporter for the daily newspaper *Verona Views*. It is the morning after Romeo and Juliet's double suicide. Your task is to cover their tragic deaths in a three-paragraph news story.

   Below is a model for organizing your report.

   First paragraph: Begin your article with a brief firsthand report of the actual events. What happened? Where? When? To whom? How? Mention only the most important facts.

   Second paragraph: Give more details about the event. Who discovered the bodies? What did that person observe? Who told the authorities? What steps have the authorities taken to investigate the deaths?

   Third paragraph: What information has been gathered about the two who died? What led up to the deaths? Who are the survivors?

   Be sure to provide a striking headline for your news story.

2. Write a three-paragraph essay based on one of your Response Logs in this workbook. Review your opinions and ideas in each Response Log. Select one of the responses that you feel strongly about.

   Follow this design or form for your essay.

   First paragraph: State your feeling or opinion. (This is your central idea or your thesis.) Be sure to give the name of the play and its author in this paragraph. Make your introduction lively so that your reader will want to continue. This will be a short paragraph, probably about three or four sentences.

   Second paragraph: Give some proof or examples that support your opinion. This paragraph should be about five or six sentences long.

   Third paragraph: Now summarize your argument and restate your thesis in a strong and new way. This paragraph should be one to three sentences long.